Friend or Foe?
Two Athletes Compete for One Olympic Dream

Debra Hess

Some of the dialogue in this play has been invented.
But the story is based on true events.

SCHOLASTIC INC.
New York   Toronto   London   Auckland   Sydney
Mexico City   New Delhi   Hong Kong

Cover photographs by
© Lisa Means

Interior illustrations by
Chris Müller

Gift of Love:
The Daniel Huffman Story

From an original movie screenplay

**Some of the dialog in this play has been invented.
But the story is based on true events.**

SCHOLASTIC INC.
**New York   Toronto   London   Auckland   Sydney
Mexico City   New Delhi   Hong Kong**

Characters

Narrator 1

Narrator 2

Shirlee Allison, Daniel's grandmother

Daniel Huffman, high school football star

Jeff, Daniel's friend

Coach Farkas, Daniel's football coach

Dr. Jenkins, Shirlee's doctor

Danny Allison, Daniel's grandfather

Scene 1

Narrator 1: Daniel Huffman, 15, spent the last year living with his mom in Florida. Things didn't work out, and now he's come back to live with his grandparents in Illinois.

Narrator 2: As he pulls into the driveway, his grandmother Shirlee is waiting for him. She comes running across the yard with her arms wide-open.

Shirlee: My handsome football star is back home with us again!

Narrator 1: Shirlee and her husband, Danny, have taken care of Daniel for most of his life.

Daniel: I smell peach pie. Did you make me one, Gran?

Shirlee: No. I made you three. And roast chicken and spaghetti and spare ribs. Now let's eat!

Narrator 2: After dinner, Daniel's friend, Jeff, stops by.

Jeff: I'm glad you're back. Did you know that football tryouts are tomorrow? We got a new coach. They say he's real tough.

Daniel: If you're trying to scare me, forget it. I've been waiting for this my whole life. I'm ready to play.

Jeff: No offense, but you look kind of out of shape to me.

Daniel: Yeah, well I didn't get a chance to do much training in Florida, but I'll be fine.

How would you describe Daniel's relationship with his grandparents?

Scene 2

Narrator 1: The next day, Daniel and Jeff go to the tryouts. Coach Farkas shows up late.

Coach: Why are you guys just sitting around? First lesson: When you are on this field, you move. Do you hear me? Now, let's get started.

Narrator 2: Daniel works hard at tryouts, but he's out of shape. He doesn't make the team. He's devastated. The next morning Shirlee finds him sleeping late.

Shirlee: Wake up! You're going to be late for football practice!

Daniel: I got cut.

Shiree: What happened?

Daniel: I'm out of shape. That's what happened. Leave me alone.

Shirlee: No way! Get up! We've got things to do. Let's go!

Narrator 1: Shirlee decides to train Daniel herself, and find a way to get him on the team.

Shirlee: Let's see how fast you can run a mile.

Daniel: What's the point of this?

Shirlee: I'm only going to tell you this once. I was a smart kid, like you. I dreamed of going to college, making something of myself, but it didn't happen. I gave up too easily. I'm not going to let you do that.

Daniel: OK. OK. I'll do it.

Narrator 2: Shirlee trains Daniel every day.

Narrator 1: Early one Sunday, Daniel is doing sprints on the school track as Shirlee times him. Coach Farkas walks up to Shirlee. They watch Daniel run.

Coach: It looks like you've done a great job with the kid, Mrs. …

Shirlee: Shirlee Allison. Daniel is my grandson.

Coach: Well, Shirlee, you know he didn't make the team.

Shirlee: I know. But the bottom line is that he's worked hard, and now he's looking good.

Narrator 2: The coach calls Daniel over.

Coach: I'm going to give you a shot, Daniel. I need a linebacker.

Daniel: Thank you! You won't regret it, Coach.

How did Daniel's grandmother convince him to keep trying?

Scene 3

Narrator 1: By his junior year, Daniel is the team's star linebacker. One day, Coach Farkas calls him into his office.

Coach: So, Daniel, what are your plans when you graduate?

Daniel: It's my dream to play college ball for the Florida State Seminoles.

Coach: Oh, you mean Bobby's team?

Daniel: You know Coach Bobby Bowden? He's a legend!

Coach: Yeah, we go back a long way. I'd say you've got a shot at making his team. I'll talk to him.

Narrator 2: By mid-season, Daniel has helped put his team in first place.

How does Daniel feel about playing football?

Scene 4

Narrator 1: But things are not going well for Shirlee. She starts feeling weak and tired.

Narrator 2: Daniel takes her to the doctor.

Dr. Jenkins: I wish I had better news for you, Shirlee. It's your diabetes. It's shutting your kidneys down. You need a kidney transplant.

Shirlee: No way! I don't want some stranger's kidney.

Dr. Jenkins: I have to be honest with you, Shirlee. It's really the only option we have left. Even with this option, there is a long waiting list, and there is no guarantee that you will get a kidney in time.

Narrator 1: Daniel can't believe it. He feels he would be lost without his grandmother.

Narrator 2: A few weeks later, Daniel and Jeff toss around the football and talk.

Jeff: How's your grandmother doing?

Daniel: Not too well. They put her on a waiting list for a kidney, but they say some people die waiting. I've been doing a lot of research about transplants. And ... well ... I could donate a kidney to my grandma.

Jeff: You? Don't you need both of your kidneys?

Daniel: No, you only need one to survive. The only thing is, I wouldn't be able to play football ever again. It would be too dangerous.

What decision does Daniel face?

Scene 5

Narrator 1: The next day, Daniel tells Shirlee his idea.

Shirlee: Are you crazy? With one kidney, there's no way you could play football. Football is what's going to get you to college. That's my dream, to see you achieve what I couldn't.

Daniel: Gran, a lot of people need you. If you won't do this for yourself, do it for them.

Shirlee: We shouldn't fight about this. We might not even match. We have to be the same blood type. Even our cells have to be built the same way.

Daniel: Well, let's find out how good a match we are.

Shirlee: Ok, Daniel. We'll see.

Why doesn't Daniel's grandma want him to donate his kidney?

Scene 6

Narrator 2: Daniel goes to the hospital and goes through many painful tests to find out if he can be a donor for Shirlee.

Narrator 1: When Daniel returns home, Shirlee is so weak she can barely stand up. A few days later, she gets a phone call.

Shirlee: That was Dr. Jenkins. She got the test results. We're almost a perfect match.

Daniel: This is awesome!

Shirlee: No, it's not. I was hoping we wouldn't match, so we could put an end to this. I won't ruin your dreams! I won't do it!

Narrator 2: This is too much for Daniel. He starts to cry.

Daniel: You've got to do it. Please don't die. I don't know what I'd do without you, Gran.

Narrator 1: Shirlee thinks for a long time. Then she takes Daniel's hands.

Shirlee: All right. I'll do it.

How does Daniel feel about his grandma?

Scene 7

Narrator 2: Several days later, the doctors perform the operation, taking out one of Daniel's kidneys and transplanting it into Shirlee. When Daniel wakes up, his grandpa is there with him.

Danny: How do you feel?

Daniel: Fine. How's Gran?

Danny: She's fine. But really, how are you? Does it hurt?

Daniel: Only when I breathe.

Narrator 1: Over the next two months, Daniel and Shirlee heal from the surgery. Shirlee makes a full recovery. Daniel recovers, too, but he misses football a lot.

What do you think Daniel will do now?

Scene 8

Narrator 2: At the end of the year, Daniel's team is still in first place, but he can't bear to watch the games. Shirlee demands that he go to the last game of the season anyway.

Daniel: Why do I have to be here?

Shirlee: The coach said he needs to see you.

Coach: Huffman! Come here!

Narrator 1: Reluctantly, Daniel walks over.

Coach: Huffman, put on your pads and jersey.

Jeff: I have a bad headache. You can take my place. I'm coming out of the game.

Daniel: What's going on here?

Coach: You can't miss out on this game.

Nobody'll hit you. You'll be fine.

Narrator 2: Daniel joins his teammates on the field. His heart pounds with excitement.

Narrator 1: Finally, the whistle blows. The game ends, and the crowd goes wild. It takes Daniel a moment to realize that they're cheering for him.

Why do you think the coach put Daniel back in the game?

Epilogue

Today, Daniel's grandmother is in good health. When she first got out of the hospital she ran an ad in the local newspaper that said:

> *My Hero,*
> *My Grandson*
> *Daniel Huffman*
> *Thanks for the new kidney and life.*
> *I didn't think we could be any closer.*
> *I was wrong.*
> *I love you,*
> *Gran Allison*

With help from his hero Bobby Bowden, Daniel got a scholarship to attend Florida State. He became student manager of their football team, the Seminoles. He plans to be a sports publicist.

Daniel has no regrets. He says, "If you love someone and you can help them, any way you can, you're going to do it."

Characters

Narrator 1

Master Jin Won Kim, Esther's father and tae kwon do master

Kay Poe, Tae kwon do competitor and Esther's friend

Mother, Kay Poe's mother

Narrator 2

Father, Kay Poe's father

Boy

Girl

Esther Kim, Tae kwon do competitor and Kay's friend

Announcer

Juan Antonio Samaranch, President of the International Olympic Committee

Referee

Interviewer

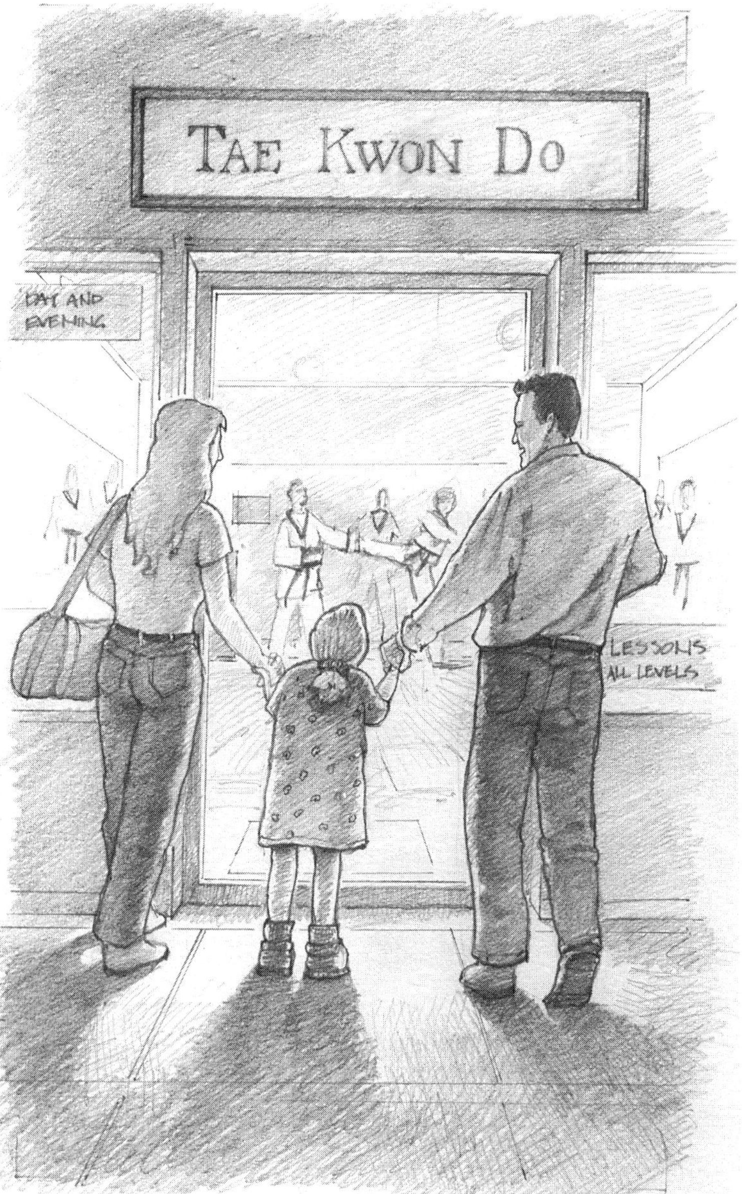
TAE KWON DO
DAY AND
EVENING
LESSONS
ALL LEVELS

Narrator 1: As the story begins, Kay is five years old. A new tae kwon do school has just opened in Kay's neighborhood. Kay is interested in trying something new. Her parents take her there to watch a class and meet the teacher, Master Jin Won Kim.

Master Kim: Do you know anything about tae kwon do, Kay?

Kay: No.

Master Kim: Well, *tae* means "to kick and jump." *Kwon* means "to strike or block with the fist" and *do* means "the way of." If you put it all together it basically means "the art of kicking and punching."

Kay: Wow!

Master Kim: Tae kwon do is a fighting sport. But we do not use weapons. And you are not allowed to kick or hit your opponent in the head. (*Turning to Kay's mother,*) But we wear helmets for protection, just in case.

Mother: That's good.

Narrator 2: Master Kim smiles.

Master Kim: But tae kwon do is not just about kicking and punching. It is about being in tune with your body and your mind. And it is also about honor.

Kay: Honor?

Master Kim: You are young. But you will learn. You will learn to fight. And you will learn to have respect for yourself and others.

Father: Do you think you want to try tae kwon do, Kay?

Kay: Sure. It looks fun!

Narrator 1: Kay starts tae kwon do classes that summer. She loves the sport and is good at it. But when she takes her first test to get a belt in tae kwon do, she is surprised.

Father: How did the test go, honey?

Kay: OK, I guess. It was weird.

Mother: What do you mean?

Kay: Well, Master Kim had me do all the fighting stuff. And he asked me all kinds of questions about tae kwon do. But he also asked me other stuff like, "Do you know your parents' birthdays?" and, "Do you clean your own room?"

Mother: Really? Why?

Kay: He said he was trying to find out what kind of a person I am. He says that's just as important as how well I fight.

Father: Do you think he's right?

Narrator 1: Kay shrugs her shoulders.

What kind of person would remember her parents' birthdays and clean her own room?

Scene 2

Narrator 2: Kay keeps taking tae kwon do. In October of that year, she goes to a costume party at Master Kim's school.

Narrator 1: Esther is Master Kim's daughter. She overhears some kids talking.

Boy: Kay looks so stupid with that new haircut.

Girl: Good thing she has that ninja costume on to cover it up.

Boy: Yeah, but she'll have to take it off sometime.

Esther: Daddy, why are those kids saying mean things about that girl?

Master Kim: Children don't always understand

how important it is to be kind. Why don't you go over and talk to her. She is our guest.

Esther: Okay, Dad. Maybe later.

Narrator 2: Kay wanders around the party sadly. She doesn't want to talk to any of the other kids. They are avoiding her, anyway. Finally, she walks over to Esther's dad.

Kay: Hello, sir.

Master Kim: Hello, Kay. That's a very nice costume. Are you having a good time?

Narrator 1: Kay shrugs her shoulders.

Master Kim: Why don't you go talk to my daughter. She's over there. Her name is Esther. She's about three years older than you. And she's very nice.

Narrator 2: Kay walks over to Esther and slips her hand into Esther's hand.

Kay: Hi!

Narrator 2: Esther is surprised, but she doesn't pull her hand away from Kay. For the rest of the party, Kay stays by Esther's side.

Narrator 1: For Esther and Kay, that party was the beginning of an incredible friendship.

Why do you think Esther decided to be nice to Kay?

Scene 3

Narrator 2: Although Esther was three years older than Kay, the girls became training partners. Their grew to be close friends.

Narrator 1: One day, Esther's father told Esther and Kay he wanted to speak to them.

Master Kim: Girls, you are getting older now. And you are both becoming skilled at tae kwon do. I want you to think about competing.

Kay: You mean fighting against other kids in tournaments?

Master Kim: Yes. You would compete in different classes because of the differences in your weight. Kay, you would compete in the finweight class. Esther, you would compete in the flyweight class.

Esther: But we wouldn't have to fight each other, right?

Master Kim: Not in competition. But I still want you two to train together. You are both excellent fighters. But you could be better. You need to train harder if you want to compete and win.

Kay: Let's do it, Esther. Let's compete. I want to win a medal.

Esther: Me too!

Narrator 2: The girls practice every day. They enter competitions. As new competitors, they don't always win. But they both love the sport, and they keep practicing.

Why won't Kay and Esther have to fight each other in competition?

Scene 4

Narrator 1: Kay is now 14 and Esther is 16. All their hard work is starting to pay off. They are both winning competitions in their weight classes.

Narrator 2: One day, in 1996, Kay comes flying into the house.

Kay: Mom, Dad—I did it! I did it!

Mother: What did you do?

Kay: I made it onto the U.S. National Team. I did it! I'm going to Cuba to compete!

Father: That's wonderful, Kay. Your mother and I are so very proud of you.

Narrator 1: In Cuba, Kay wins a silver medal. Over the next four years, Kay wins

both gold and silver medals in the National Championships and Junior Olympic competitions.

Narrator 2: Esther also wins gold and silver medals in both National and Junior Olympic championships.

Narrator 1: In 1999, Master Kim made an announcement to both girls that would change their lives.

Master Kim: Girls, I am entering you both for the Olympic qualification trials.

Kay: Do you think we're good enough?

Master Kim: I know you are good enough. You are both capable of winning gold medals for your country. But you must train harder than ever. Are you up to it?

Kay: Are you kidding? The Olympics?

Esther: We're going to the Olympics!

Narrator 2: The girls start screaming and jumping and hugging each other.

Master Kim: Girls, girls. You are not going to

the Olympics yet. You must qualify to make the team. There are many competitions ahead of you before you can go to Australia.

Kay: What do you think, Esther?

Esther: Who can stop us?

Master Kim: There is one more thing. The Olympic committee has made a decision that affects you both.

Esther: What is it?

Master Kim: They have combined the flyweight and finweight classes into one class.

Kay: Oh, no! That means we're in the same class now.

Esther: That means we'll have to compete against each other.

Kay: I don't think I can do it.

Master Kim: Look, girls. You are both winners. And now you both have a chance to win the Olympic gold medal.

Kay: But I don't want to fight against Esther.

Master Kim: You have trained together for years. You can do this.

Esther: But she's my best friend!

Master Kim: This isn't about friendship. It is about competition. You both have warrior spirits. And you both have a chance to go to the Olympics. There is one spot open.

Narrator 1: After Esther's father leaves the room, the girls hug.

Kay: You will always be my best friend, Esther. No matter what.

Esther: Nothing will ever change that.

Would you find it hard to compete against a friend? Why or why not?

Scene 5

Narrator 2: It's a warm May day in 2000. Both girls have trained hard to get a chance to make the Olympic team. The first competition is a round-robin match. All the Olympic hopefuls must fight the others in their class. Esther and Kay fight. It's a close decision, but Kay is the winner.

Narrator 1: Then another round of matches begin. Esther Kim and Kay Poe stand together beside a tae kwon do ring. Esther has already made it into the finals. Kay is about to fight. The winner of Kay's match will face Esther.

Esther: This is it, Kay. You can do it. If you win this one we'll both be in the finals.

Kay: That's right. If I win, I have to fight against you, Esther. I still don't want to.

Esther: But you will. After you win this match, you and I will enter the ring together. We'll both do our best. We're both champions.

Kay: You're the best friend I've ever had.

Esther: You, too. Go in there and win.

Narrator 2: Kay puts her helmet on and enters the ring.

Announcer: The semi-final match of women's tae kwon do is about to begin. Now entering the ring are Kay Poe and Mandy Meloon.

Narrator 1: The crowd is hushed as the fight begins. It's a close match. In the stands, Esther holds her breath, quietly rooting for her friend to win.

Announcer: Kay Poe has fallen! She's clutching her knee. She appears to be hurt.

Narrator 2: Kay made eye contact with Esther in the crowd. Kay's eyes were watering with pain. "You can still win this fight!" Esther mouthed to her friend.

Announcer: Wait! It looks like Kay Poe is getting up. She's back in the fight!

Narrator 1: Kay finishes the fight with energy and skill. The judges decide in her favor. The crowd cheers. Esther jumps up to find her friend and congratulate her.

What do you think winning this match says about Kay's fighting spirit?

Scene 6

Narrator 2: After the match, Kay hobbled off the mat and collapsed in Master Kim's arms.

Esther: What happened?

Narrator 1: Master Kim lays Kay down on an exercise mat. Tears are streaming down Kay's face. Esther kneels down beside her friend.

Esther: Kay, you won!

Kay: I know.

Narrator 2: But Kay doesn't stop crying. Esther glances at her friend's leg. Kay's knee is bruised and swollen.

Esther: Kay—oh no! Your knee! Look at your knee.

Narrator 1: Master Kim examines Kay's knee.

Master Kim: Kay, your knee is dislocated.

Esther: What are we going to do?

Kay: We're going to fight. What do you mean? What else can we do?

Esther: Kay, you can't fight like this.

Narrator 1: Esther studies her friend, then she looks up at her father. She knows what she must do.

Narrator 2: Esther knows her father will support her decision. He has given them so many lessons in honor.

Esther: Listen, Kay...

Kay: What?

Esther: Kay, don't argue. Just listen. I'm going to bow out. I can't fight you this way. You can't even stand up.

Kay: But you can't bow out! You want this as much as I do.

Esther: I love you, Kay. And I support you. Both of us are winners. I want you to take that spot.

Narrator 2: Tears are still streaming down Kay's face.

Kay: Esther, I just can't ask you to do that.

Esther: Look Kay, this is the right thing for me to do. I couldn't live with myself fighting you like this. Remember the commandments of tae kwon do?

Kay: You mean the one about loyalty?

Esther: Loyalty and respect. You are my friend. This is what I want.

Kay: Esther, there's no one that I've ever known in my entire lifetime that would do this for me.

Master Kim: Kay, you compete for Esther and do your best, OK?

Kay: Yes, sir.

Narrator 1: Kay is no longer the only one crying.

If you had been in Esther's place, what would you have done?

Scene 7

Narrator 1: Esther helps her friend walk as the two girls return to the ring. Master Kim goes to speak with the judges.

Announcer: Ladies and Gentlemen, we have an announcement. Esther Kim is bowing out of the next match. Kay Poe has just won a spot on the Olympic team.

Narrator 2: The referee enters the ring and holds up Kay's hand.

Referee: The winner!

Narrator 1: Esther holds up Kay's other hand and smiles at her friend. There are tears streaming down the faces of both girls.

Narrator 2: The audience explodes. There is cheering and clapping. Many people are

crying. Esther and Kay hug. Then Esther helps her friend down from the ring.

Kay: Thank you, Esther.

Esther: I'm going to make you work so hard. No matter how much you cry, I'm going to keep pushing you. You're going to win gold for us both!

How would you describe the kind of person Esther is?

Scene 8

Narrator 1: The next morning, Esther is asleep. The phone rings.

Esther: Hello?

Samaranch: Is this Esther Kim?

Esther: Yes.

Samaranch: Esther, this is Juan Antonio Samaranch. I'm the President of the International Olympic Committee.

Narrator 2: Esther sits bolt upright in bed. She is so excited, her voice cracks as she speaks.

Esther: Hi, Mr. Samaranch. Yes, I know who you are.

Samaranch: I was very impressed with your show of sportsmanship, Esther. I'm sorry you

won't be going to the Olympics to fight on the team with Kay.

Esther: Me, too. But I'll watch on the television and I'll cheer Kay from here. I'm sure she'll win.

Samaranch: I would like to invite you and your father to come to Sydney to watch Kay in person. I will pay for your plane tickets.

Why do you think Juan Samaranch wants to do this for Esther?

Scene 9

Narrator 1: By the time the Olympics arrive, Kay's knee has healed. Kay and Esther travel with their parents to Sydney, Australia.

Narrator 2: Finally, the day of Kay's Olympic match arrives. Esther sits in the stands with Kay's parents and her father and watches, praying for her friend to win a gold medal.

Announcer: Kay Poe of the United States of America and Hanne Hoegh Poulsen of Denmark are about to begin the first round.

Narrator 1: Kay attacks first and scores.

Esther: Come on, Kay!

Narrator 2: Kay fights her best. By the end of the second round, she is winning 3 to 1.

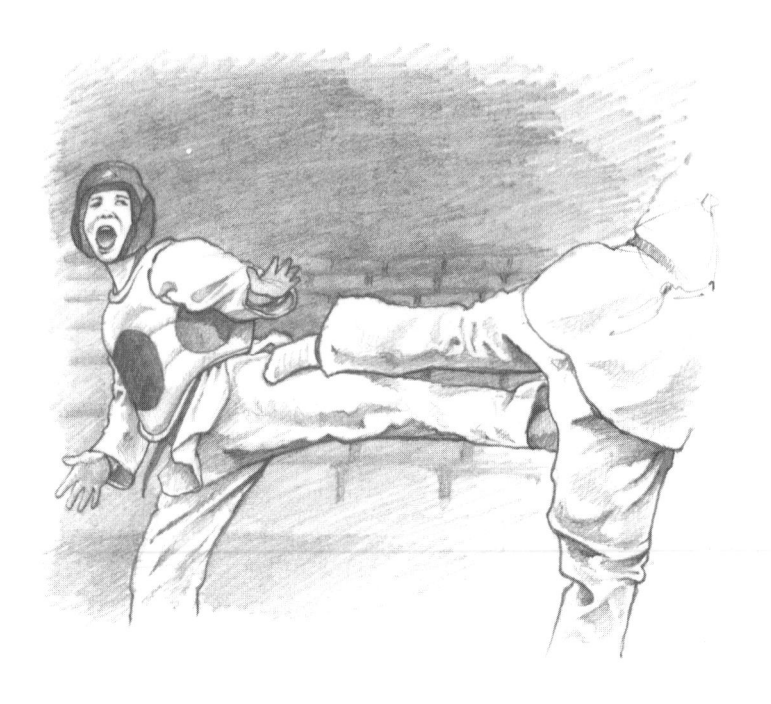

Narrator 1: But Hanne fights back fearlessly. At the end of the match, the score is 4 to 3. Hanne Hoegh Poulsen of Denmark has won.

Narrator 2: Kay and Esther's dream of winning a medal in Australia is over.

How do you think Kay feels about her defeat?

Scene 10

Interviewer: Kay, can you tell me how you feel about not winning a medal in the Olympics?

Kay: I lost. It happens to the best of athletes. But I guess, when I think about how hard it was to get here, and all that I went through to get here, I do feel, an extra disappointment.

Interviewer: As of now, do you or Esther have any plans to compete in the 2004 Olympics?

Kay: I don't know. I think I'm going back to college. I'm not sure what Esther will do. All I know is that she is the best friend a girl could have. She will always be in my heart.

Do you think Esther and Kay should have handled things differently? Explain.

Epilogue

Kay Poe is planning to compete again in the 2004 Olympics in Athens, Greece. She is considered the world's strongest women fighter in her weight class.

Esther Kim is studying business and fashion design at the University of Houston. "I'm going on 15 years in tae kwon do," Esther says. "I really want to start living a normal life and doing the things I haven't been able to do."

Today, Kay and Esther's friendship is as strong as ever.